Piano Exam Pieces

ABRSM Grade 5

Selected from the 2013 & 2014 syllabus

Name  Kirstie

CW00350347

Date of exam

Contents

Editor for ABRSM: Richard Jones

CD			page
		LIST A	
1	1	**Johann Christoph Friedrich Bach** Allegretto in F: from *Musikalische Nebenstunden*	2
2	2	**Ludwig van Beethoven** Minuet in D: No. 7 from 12 Minuets, WoO 7	4
3	③	**George Frideric Handel** Allemande in A minor, HWV 478	6
		LIST B	
7	1	**Edward MacDowell** To a Wild Rose: No. 1 from *Woodland Sketches*, Op. 51	8
8	2	**Robert Schumann** *** : No. 26 from *Album für die Jugend*, Op. 68	10
9	③	**Francisco Tárrega** Adelita	12
		LIST C	
13	1	**Darius Brubeck** For Lydia	14
14	②	**Dmitry Borisovich Kabalevsky** Kavaleriiskaya: No. 29 from *30 detskikh p'es*, Op. 27	16
15	3	**Heitor Villa-Lobos** Samba-lelê: No. 4 from *Guia prático*, Album 2	18

Other pieces for Grade 5

LIST A

4	④	**Bolck** Allegro vivo: 3rd movt from Sonatina in G, Op. 59 No. 2. No. 21 from *Das neue Sonatinenbuch*, Vol. 1 (Schott)
5	5	**J. G. Krebs** Allegro in G. No. 11 from *Kleine leichte Clavierstücke* (Schott)
6	⑥	**Rameau** La Joyeuse. *Bärenreiter Piano Album – Baroque* (Bärenreiter)

LIST B

10	④	**Gedike** Miniature, Op. 8 No. 7: No. 11 from *Russian Music for Piano*, Book 3 (Chester)
11	5	**Palmgren** Vestfinsk Dans (West-Finnish Dance): No. 5 from *Finska rytmer*, Op. 31 (Hansen) or (piece published individually: Hansen)
12	6	**Tchaikovsky** Douce rêverie (Daydream): No. 21 from *Album for the Young*, Op. 39 (ABRSM) or *More Romantic Pieces for Piano*, Book 2 (ABRSM)

LIST C

16	④	**A. Benjamin** Haunted House. *Animations: 27 Pieces on the Lively Side* (Boosey & Hawkes)
17	5	**Milhaud** Modéré: No. 1 from *Quatre romances sans paroles* (Salabert)
18	6	**Christopher Norton** Sierra: No. 4 from *The Christopher Norton Rock Preludes Collection* (Boosey & Hawkes)

First published in 2012 by ABRSM (Publishing) Ltd, a wholly owned subsidiary of ABRSM, 24 Portland Place, London W1B 1LU, United Kingdom © 2012 by The Associated Board of the Royal Schools of Music

Music origination by Julia Bovee
Cover by Kate Benjamin & Andy Potts
Printed in England by Halstan & Co. Ltd, Amersham, Bucks.

MIX
Paper from responsible sources
FSC™ C109619

A:1

Allegretto in F

from *Musikalische Nebenstunden*

Edited by Timothy Roberts

J. C. F. Bach
(1732–95)

Musikalische Nebenstunden Musical Leisure Hours

Johann Christoph Friedrich Bach, the second youngest son of Johann Sebastian Bach, entered the service of Count Wilhelm of Schaumburg-Lippe in Bückeburg in 1750. He was promoted to the post of Konzertmeister in 1759 and remained at the court for the rest of his life. He was admired as a keyboard virtuoso as well as a composer.

The collection from which this Allegretto is selected contains not only keyboard pieces but also cantatas and songs. According to Timothy Roberts, editor of the ABRSM edition, short pieces such as this were intended for light entertainment and perhaps also as teaching pieces for the flourishing amateur market.

In this Allegretto, ornament realizations are based on the composer's own instructions. **The ornament on the last note of bb. 5 and 6, and in parallel places elsewhere, may be simplified or omitted in the exam.** All staccato dots are editorial suggestions only.

Minuet in D

No. 7 from 12 Minuets, WoO 7

Ludwig van Beethoven
(1770–1827)

[Fine]

Beethoven's 12 Minuets, WoO 7, belong to his early period in Vienna (1792–1802), during which he established a formidable reputation as a brilliant young pianist and composer, playing regularly in the homes of the Viennese aristocracy. The original orchestral version of this collection was composed free of charge, 'out of love for his fellow artists', for a masked ball held by the Pension Society of Viennese Artists on St Cecilia's Day (22 November) 1795. Owing to the great popularity of Beethoven's dances, they were repeated at the same event two years later, on 26 November 1797. The piano reduction of the minuets, of which No. 7 is selected here, appeared only three weeks after the original masked ball of 1795 – another sign of their great success. In No. 7 characteristic Beethovenian touches are already found – for example, the *fortissimo* chords on the flat supertonic in bb. 13–14.

Source: *XII Menuetten im Clavierauszug* (Vienna: Artaria, 1795)

Trio

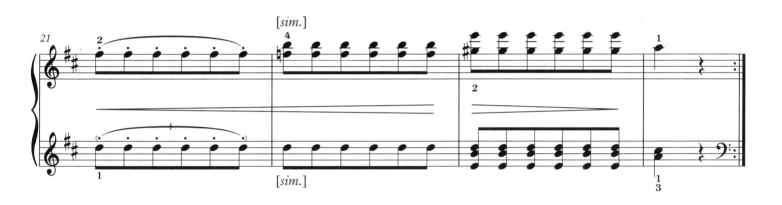

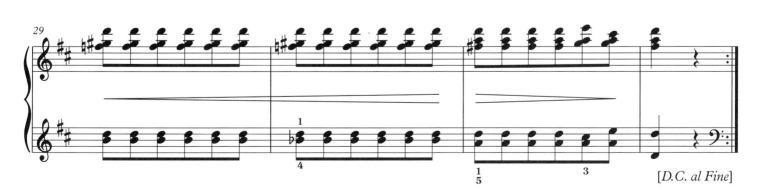

[D.C. al Fine]

Allemande in A minor

HWV 478

G. F. Handel
(1685–1759)

This *allemande* is one of Handel's earliest keyboard pieces, composed around 1705 when he was only 20 and living in the North German city of Hamburg. There he played violin and later harpsichord in the Hamburg Opera. At that time, too, he composed keyboard pieces, arias, cantatas, and his first opera *Almira*.

The *allemande* is a Baroque dance that became a stylized keyboard piece, either on its own, as here, or as the first movement of the standard suite. It is normally in quadruple time and moderately slow in tempo. The early 18th-century theorist J. G. Walther said that the *allemande* 'is a serious and dignified movement and should be so performed.'

The source contains a number of obvious errors, which have been corrected without comment. Dynamics are left to the player's discretion. Source: MS copy, London, British Library, R.M.18.b.8.

AB 3632

B:1

To a Wild Rose

No. 1 from *Woodland Sketches*, Op. 51

Edward MacDowell
(1860–1908)

The American composer Edward MacDowell studied in France and Germany, receiving encouragement from Liszt, who was impressed by some of his compositions. He returned to America in 1888, working as a teacher and composer in Boston till 1896, when he was appointed professor of music at Columbia University.

MacDowell's *Woodland Sketches*, Op. 51, from which this piece is selected, was one of the last fruits of his Boston period: the sketches were composed in 1896, published in the same year, and the collection soon became one of his most popular works. In order to manage the large stretches in bb. 41–4, players might spread the first left-hand chord (b. 41), then use the pedal to sustain the long *A* beneath the melodic crotchets. Source: *Woodland Sketches*, Op. 51 (Boston: P. L. Jung, 1896)

.

No. 26 from *Album für die Jugend*, Op. 68

Robert Schumann
(1810–56)

Nicht schnell, hübsch vorzutragen ♩ = 88
[Not fast, played prettily]

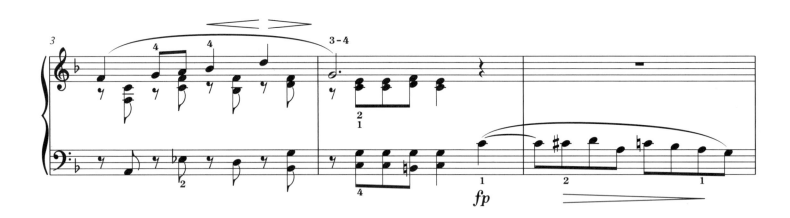

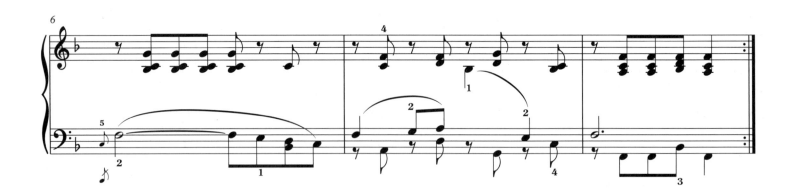

Album für die Jugend Album for the Young

Robert Schumann's *Album for the Young*, Op. 68, was composed in less than a month in 1848. At the time, the composer wrote: 'I don't remember ever having been in such good musical form…The pieces simply poured out, one after another.' Some of the 42 pieces in the collection were dedicated to Schumann's daughter Marie on her seventh birthday.

   This piece is selected from Part II, which is designed for rather more grown-up young people than Part I. It was left untitled by the composer as *.*. In the first edition, supervised by Schumann and published in 1848, the pieces are collectively entitled 'Clavierstücke' (Piano Pieces). The metronome mark is by Schumann's wife Clara.

Source: *43 [sic] Clavierstücke für die Jugend*, Op. 68 (Hamburg: Schuberth & Co., 1850)

Adapted from Schumann: *Album für die Jugend*, Op. 68, edited by Howard Ferguson (ABRSM)

AB 3632

Etwas langsamer
[Somewhat slower]

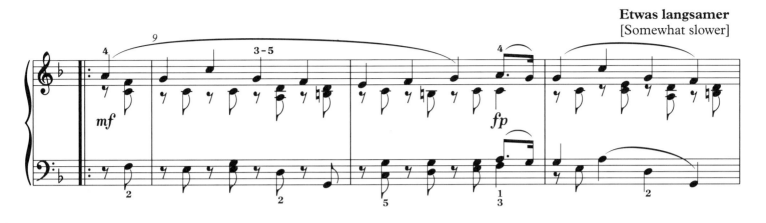

Im Tempo
[In tempo]

Adelita

Edited by Nancy Bachus

Francisco Tárrega
(1852–1909)

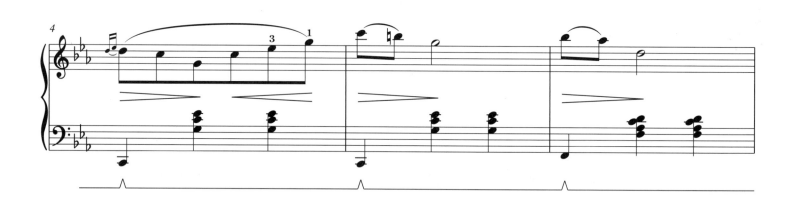

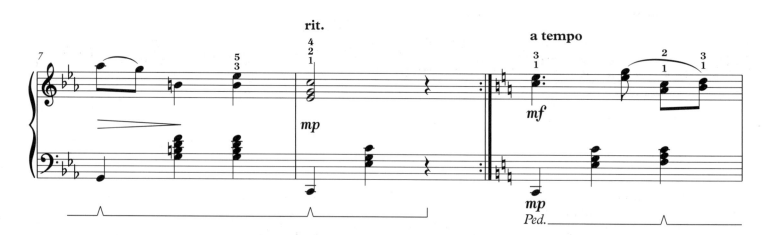

The Spanish guitarist, teacher and composer Francisco Tárrega entered the Madrid Conservatory to study piano and composition in 1874. He settled in Barcelona in 1885. Tárrega not only composed much guitar music but transcribed for the instrument music by Beethoven, Mendelssohn and Chopin, as well as that of his compatriots Albéniz and Granados. He is credited with having established the foundations of modern classical guitar technique.

This romantic, waltz-style piece is a piano arrangement of an original for the guitar. Grace notes are perhaps best played before the beat. In b. 14 'molto ten.' indicates that the right-hand quaver 3rds should be held for their full value and perhaps slightly prolonged.

For Lydia

Darius Brubeck
(born 1947)

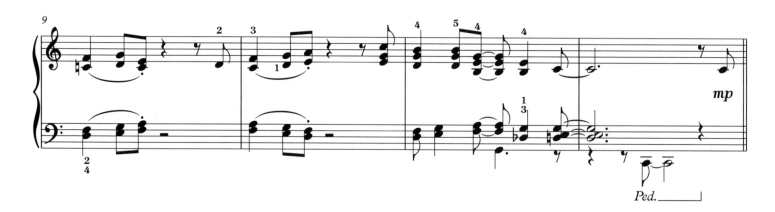

Darius Brubeck, the son of Dave Brubeck, is an American jazz keyboard player. In the 1970s he toured with the New Brubeck Quartet. He taught in South Africa from 1983 to 2006, and in 1989 was appointed professor of jazz studies and director of the Centre for Jazz and Popular Music at the University of KwaZulu-Natal. Currently he teaches and performs in Europe, and his present group, the Darius Brubeck Quartet, is based in London.

This piece, with its highly inventive harmonies, was written for Brubeck's granddaughter Lydia when she was 12. The composer has written: 'The melody is pretty, even basic, but beneath this simple diatonic surface, chromatic harmony and inversions add colour and complexity. Rhythm patterns in the left hand (played straight) create momentum under the slow melody line. There are skills to be learnt here: the hands work together *and* separately, on and off the beat. Metronomic precision, natural dynamic expression and relaxation will follow. *For Lydia* is not without challenges, but it didn't take her long to learn it.'

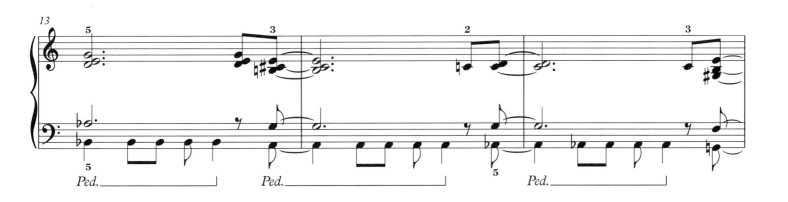

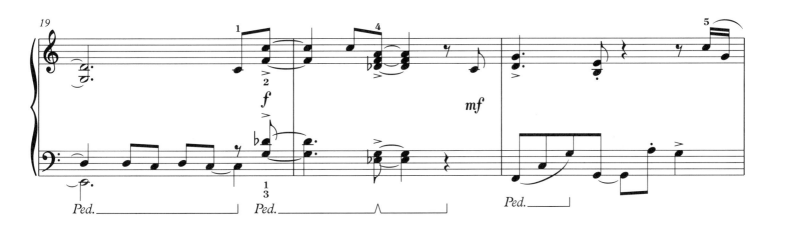

Кавалерийская
No. 29 from 30 детских пьес, Op. 27

Kavaleriiskaya

No. 29 from *30 detskikh p'es*, Op. 27

DO NOT PHOTOCOPY
© MUSIC

C:2

D. B. Kabalevsky
(1904–87)

Kavaleriiskaya Cavalryman; **Detskikh p'es** Children's Pieces

The Russian composer Dmitry Borisovich Kabalevsky studied piano and composition at the Moscow Conservatory, where he later taught, being appointed professor in 1939. As writer, teacher, composer and administrator, he became a major figure in Soviet music of the 20th century. He was active in the field of music education and wrote much music for children, including the *30 Children's Pieces*, Op. 27, from which 'Cavalryman' is selected.

In his performance notes to the Boosey & Hawkes edition, John York has given the following advice: 'Keep the rhythm precise and forward-looking, disciplined but ready for action. There is an enormous wealth of interesting detail in this piece, and it will have tremendous success in performance if every detail is worked out at a slow tempo first. The dynamic range should be wide.'

C:3

Samba-lelê

No. 4 from *Guia prático*, Album 2

Heitor Villa-Lobos
(1887–1959)

Guia prático Practical Guide

Heitor Villa-Lobos was the best-known and most admired Brazilian composer of the 20th century. Immensely prolific, he united the techniques of contemporary European art music with elements of the folk and popular music of his native country. In the 1930s and early 1940s he was much concerned with music education and for this purpose used many traditional Brazilian songs he had collected as the basis of his *Guia prático*. Under this title he published a choral album and 11 piano albums.

   In this piece, the *dal segno* instruction should not be observed in the exam. In the left hand of bb. 12 and 14 etc. the pedal may be used to sustain the lower chord while the hand moves to the note or chord above.

D.S. al Fine

[Fine]